M000276116

THIS JOURNAL BELONGS TO:

Laura

Harry Potter™

WISDOM

A GUIDED JOURNAL FOR
EMBRACING YOUR INNER

RAVENCLAW™

STUDIO PRESS

INTRODUCTION

WISE. WITTY. CREATIVE. These are the traits of Ravenclaw house, the cleverest house at Hogwarts, draped in its graceful colours of blue and silver and represented by a raven. There are many notable and beloved Ravenclaw characters in the Harry Potter films. From Luna Lovegood and Cho Chang to renowned wandmaker Mr. Ollivander, Ravenclaws are represented by a wide range of witches and wizards. But what does it mean to truly be a Ravenclaw? How can you bring out your qualities of wisdom, wit and creativity and apply them to your everyday life?

This journal, composed of 52 weeks of prompts, will help you reflect on, connect with and develop the Ravenclaw inside you. Each week includes two kinds of prompts. The first is a simple form where you can record daily acts of wisdom, wit or creativity. Taking the structure of a simple "one-line-a-day" journal, this form allows you to record small "Ravenclaw moments" that you encounter throughout your week. There is no pressure to fill one out every day. After all, you may not have the opportunity to excercise your wisdom every day. But it gives you an opportunity to notice and note small ways that you embody your Ravenclaw persona. The second prompt goes deeper, referencing specific quotes, moments, places or characters from the films and inviting you to think about how being a Ravenclaw shapes and affects your life. These prompts include freewriting, letter writing, list making, colouring and more.

The Harry Potter films have inspired us, now it's time to explore further and embrace your inner Ravenclaw.

WEEK 1

RAVENCLAW MOMENTS:

Daily Acts of Wisdom, Wit and Creativity

Monday 4.1.2021

I have stuck to my healthy eating, exercised and was able to plan ahead for a new term in year two. Planning exciting lessons! 19st 2lb

Tuesday 5.1.2021

Actually received some good praise for my online work. Prepared and stayed quite calm despite a new lockdown. 19st 1lb (-1lb)

~~Wednesday~~ Monday 11.10.2021

Things are so different now, we're married! ♡ We are looking to buy a house and work is ok! I can handle it. We're going to see yungblud tomorrow. 15st 10lb

(-3st, 6lb).

Thursday

Friday

Saturday

Sunday

WEEK 1

RAVENCLAWS, LIKE LUNA LOVEGOOD, CHO CHANG and Professor Flitwick, rely on their wisdom, wit and creativity to accomplish their goals. By purposefully embracing your inner Ravenclaw qualities, you are taking active steps to realise your dreams. What are you hoping to achieve or discover by using this journal? How do you see your Ravenclaw qualities helping you do this?

I hope to find organisation and clarity. I want to use this journal as a peaceful minute, a moment of reflection. It would be great if I could use this journal to "declutter" my mind!

WEEK 2

RAVENCLAW MOMENTS:
Daily Acts of Wisdom, Wit and Creativity

Monday

_____
_____
_____
_____
_____

Tuesday

_____
_____
_____
_____
_____

Wednesday

_____
_____
_____
_____
_____

Thursday

Friday

Saturday

Sunday

COLOURING MEDITATIONS

The Sorting Hat sorts each Hogwarts student into their house on their first night at school, taking into account their background, talents, personalities and personal choice. Due to your wisdom, wit and creativity, you have been sorted into Ravenclaw. Colour in the hat below and decorate the rest of the page with iconography and embellishments that represent your identity as a Ravenclaw.

WEEK 3

RAVENCLAW MOMENTS:
Daily Acts of Wisdom, Wit and Creativity

Monday

_____
_____
_____
_____
_____

Tuesday

_____
_____
_____
_____
_____

Wednesday

_____
_____
_____
_____
_____

Thursday

Friday

Saturday

Sunday

WEEK 3

IN *HARRY POTTER AND THE PHILOSOPHER'S STONE,* Harry discovers the Mirror of Erised in an unused classroom at Hogwarts. When he looks into it, he sees his parents. As Professor Dumbledore later explains, the mirror shows the viewer whatever their heart most desires. What do you think you would see if you looked in the mirror? Do you see a connection to your identity as a Ravenclaw? What is it?

WEEK 4

RAVENCLAW MOMENTS:
Daily Acts of Wisdom, Wit and Creativity

Monday

_____
_____
_____
_____
_____

Tuesday

_____
_____
_____
_____
_____

Wednesday

_____
_____
_____
_____
_____

Thursday

Friday

Saturday

Sunday

WEEK 4

THERE ARE MANY AMAZING Ravenclaw characters in the Harry Potter films. Who is your favourite? In what way do you think this character embodies the traits of the house?

WEEK 5

RAVENCLAW MOMENTS:
Daily Acts of Wisdom, Wit and Creativity

Monday

_____
_____
_____
_____

Tuesday

_____
_____
_____
_____

Wednesday

_____
_____
_____
_____

Thursday

Friday

Saturday

Sunday

WEEK 5

"Your triumphs will earn you points. Any rule-breaking and you will lose points."

—Professor McGonagall, *Harry Potter and the Philosopher's Stone*

It's important to celebrate our victories.
Make a list of five recent accomplishments you achieved that you believe would earn you points for Ravenclaw. Award yourself with the number of points you think you earned. Good job!

1. _____

_____

_____

_____ *Points:* _____

2. _____

_____

_____

_____ *Points:* _____

3. _____

_____

_____

_____ *Points:* _____

4. _____

_____

_____

_____ *Points:* _____

5. _____

_____

_____

_____ *Points:* _____

WEEK 6

RAVENCLAW MOMENTS:
Daily Acts of Wisdom, Wit and Creativity

Monday

Tuesday

Wednesday

Thursday

Friday

Saturday

Sunday

WEEK 6

ON HARRY'S FIRST DAY AT HOGWARTS, he and Ron get lost and are late to class. As a Ravenclaw, imagine how you would spend your first day at Hogwarts.

WEEK 7

RAVENCLAW MOMENTS:
Daily Acts of Wisdom, Wit and Creativity

Monday

_____
_____
_____
_____
_____

Tuesday

_____
_____
_____
_____
_____

Wednesday

_____
_____
_____
_____
_____

Thursday

_____
_____
_____
_____

Friday

_____
_____
_____
_____

Saturday

_____
_____
_____
_____

Sunday

_____
_____
_____
_____

WEEK 7

OUR SKILLS AND TALENTS OFTEN reflect the inner qualities we naturally possess. For example, Harry is a skilled flier, a talent that could be said to reflect the Gryffindor traits of daringness and nerve. What specific skills and talents do you possess, and how do you feel they relate to your qualities as a Ravenclaw?

ABOVE: Concept art of Harry and the Firebolt by Dermot Power.

THIS PAGE: Concept art by Adam Brockbank.

WEEK 8

RAVENCLAW MOMENTS:

Daily Acts of Wisdom, Wit and Creativity

Monday

Tuesday

Wednesday

Thursday

Friday

Saturday

Sunday

WEEK 8

PROFESSOR FLITWICK is the head of Ravenclaw house during Harry's time at Hogwarts. There is no question that teachers, particularly those we work closely with, have a huge effect on the kind of person we grow up to be. Write a letter to your "head of house" – a teacher or mentor who helped you develop your Ravenclaw qualities – reflecting on what they taught you and thanking them for being part of your journey.

WEEK 9

RAVENCLAW MOMENTS:
Daily Acts of Wisdom, Wit and Creativity

Monday

Tuesday

Wednesday

Thursday

Friday

Saturday

Sunday

WEEK 9

Aside from being the head of Ravenclaw house, Professor Flitwick is also the Charms teacher at Hogwarts. In one memorable *Harry Potter and the Philosopher's Stone* scene, he teaches the first-years *Wingardium Leviosa* – the Levitation Charm. How do you think Professor Flitwick's qualities as a Ravenclaw are represented in his personality as a teacher? What do you think you could learn from him, both as a Ravenclaw and as a person?

WEEK 10

RAVENCLAW MOMENTS:
Daily Acts of Wisdom, Wit and Creativity

Monday

_____
_____
_____
_____

Tuesday

_____
_____
_____
_____

Wednesday

_____
_____
_____
_____

Thursday

Friday

Saturday

Sunday

WEEK 10

"We've all got both light and dark inside us. What matters is the part we choose to act on. That's who we really are."

—Sirius Black, *Harry Potter and the Order of the Phoenix*

Sirius Black speaks this powerful quote to Harry in *Harry Potter and the Order of the Phoenix* at a moment when Harry is feeling scared, anxious and insecure in his identity. This quote could be interpreted to mean that we all have our strong points and our weak points, our positive attributes and our flaws. Ravenclaws are usually described as wise, witty and creative. But they occasionally also have a reputation for being stuck-up. Think about two moments in your life, one when your behaviour reflected the "light" side of Ravenclaw and one when it reflected the "dark" side. Describe these events on the next page. What can you learn from them?

Light:

_____

_____

_____

_____

_____

_____

_____

_____

_____

_____

_____

Dark:

_____

_____

_____

_____

_____

_____

_____

_____

_____

_____

_____

WEEK 11

RAVENCLAW MOMENTS:
Daily Acts of Wisdom, Wit and Creativity

Monday

_____
_____
_____
_____

Tuesday

_____
_____
_____
_____

Wednesday

_____
_____
_____
_____

Thursday

_____
_____
_____
_____
_____

Friday

_____
_____
_____
_____
_____

Saturday

_____
_____
_____
_____
_____

Sunday

_____
_____
_____
_____

WEEK 11

IN *HARRY POTTER AND THE ORDER OF THE PHOENIX,* Harry meets Luna Lovegood, an open-minded, clever and quirky witch who doesn't let other people's opinions get in the way of achieving her goals. Write down three long-term goals you are currently working on. How do you see your assets as a Ravenclaw helping you accomplish these aspirations?

1. _____

_____

_____

2. _____

_____

_____

3. _____

_____

_____

WEEK 12

RAVENCLAW MOMENTS:

Daily Acts of Wisdom, Wit and Creativity

Monday

Tuesday

Wednesday

Thursday

Friday

Saturday

Sunday

WEEK 12

"*Happiness can be found, even in the darkest of times, if one only remembers to turn on the light.*"

—Professor Dumbledore, *Harry Potter and the Prisoner of Azkaban*

List ten things that bring joy to your Ravenclaw heart.
Refer back to these when you are experiencing times of trouble or stress.

1. _____

2. _____

3. _____

4. _____

5.

6.

7.

8.

9.

10.

WEEK 13

RAVENCLAW MOMENTS:
Daily Acts of Wisdom, Wit and Creativity

Monday

Tuesday

Wednesday

Thursday

Friday

Saturday

Sunday

WEEK 13

IN *HARRY POTTER AND THE DEATHLY HALLOWS – PART 1,*
Xenophilius Lovegood sells Harry and his friends out to the Death Eaters
when they arrive at his house seeking information about the Deathly
Hallows. He later tearfully explains that the Death Eaters have captured
Luna and are holding her as punishment for Xenophilius's support of
Harry in *The Quibbler*. Do you think Xenophilius made the right, or at
least the understandable, choice in that moment? Knowing what he knew
at the time, would you have made the same choice? Why or why not?

WEEK 14

RAVENCLAW MOMENTS:

Daily Acts of Wisdom, Wit and Creativity

Monday

_____
_____
_____
_____
_____

Tuesday

_____
_____
_____
_____
_____

Wednesday

_____
_____
_____
_____
_____

Thursday

Friday

Saturday

Sunday

WEEK 14

COLOURING MEDITATIONS

It's time to show some house pride. Colour the Ravenclaw
crest below, and decorate the rest of the page with embellishments
and decorations of your choosing.

WEEK 15

RAVENCLAW MOMENTS:
Daily Acts of Wisdom, Wit and Creativity

Monday

_____

_____

_____

_____

Tuesday

_____

_____

_____

_____

Wednesday

_____

_____

_____

_____

Thursday

Friday

Saturday

Sunday

WEEK 15

IN THE HARRY POTTER FILMS, Harry Potter and Draco
Malfoy are bitter rivals. Have you ever had a rivalry with another person?
Were they in the same house as you or a different one? What about this
person clashed with your traits as a Ravenclaw?

WEEK 16

RAVENCLAW MOMENTS:
Daily Acts of Wisdom, Wit and Creativity

Monday

_____
_____
_____
_____

Tuesday

_____
_____
_____
_____

Wednesday

_____
_____
_____
_____

Thursday

Friday

Saturday

Sunday

HOGWARTS CASTLE IS A MASSIVE, ancient building filled with classrooms, student living spaces, soaring bridges, deep dungeons, high towers, moving staircases and more than one secret room. Which aspect of the castle would you be most eager to explore? Do you see a connection between this choice and your identity as a Ravenclaw? How so?

THIS PAGE: Concept art of the exterior and interior of Hogwarts castle by Andrew Williamson.

CLOCKWISE FROM TOP LEFT: The exterior of Hogwarts castle by Andrew Williamson; a concept piece of the stained glass window in the prefects' bathroom by Adam Brockbank; a study of the Owlery by Andrew Williamson; a concept sketch of the second-years in Greenhouse Three by Andrew Williamson.

WEEK 17

RAVENCLAW MOMENTS:

Daily Acts of Wisdom, Wit and Creativity

Monday

Tuesday

Wednesday

Thursday

Friday

Saturday

Sunday

WEEK 17

IMAGINE YOU HAVE THE OPPORTUNITY to interview one
Ravenclaw from the Harry Potter films. Who would you choose?
Write ten questions you would ask them.

10 QUESTIONS FOR: _____

1. _____
_____
_____

2. _____
_____
_____

3. _____
_____
_____

4. _____
_____

5. _____

_____

_____

6. _____

_____

_____

7. _____

_____

_____

8. _____

_____

_____

9. _____

_____

_____

10. _____

_____

_____

WEEK 18

RAVENCLAW MOMENTS:
Daily Acts of Wisdom, Wit and Creativity

Monday

Tuesday

Wednesday

Thursday

Friday

Saturday

Sunday

WEEK 18

IN *HARRY POTTER AND THE CHAMBER OF SECRETS*,
Gilderoy Lockhart comes to Hogwarts as the new Defence Against
the Dark Arts teacher. Though he has a reputation as a great wizard
(bolstered by his books), it is eventually revealed that he is in fact
a liar who's been taking credit for other people's actions. Despite
being a Ravenclaw, his only real talent is Memory Charms, which he
uses to wipe his victim's memories – hardly an appropriate action
for a Ravenclaw. Have you ever acted in a way that went against
your house's traits? Why? Describe the circumstances below.

WEEK 19

RAVENCLAW MOMENTS:
Daily Acts of Wisdom, Wit and Creativity

Monday

Tuesday

Wednesday

Thursday

Friday

Saturday

Sunday

WEEK 19

IN THE HARRY POTTER FILMS, family members are often – but not always – placed in the same houses. While all of the Weasleys are in Gryffindor and all of the Malfoys are in Slytherin, characters like Sirius Black and Parvati and Padma Patil are placed in different houses than other members of their family. What houses would your parents and siblings belong to and why? How do you think this might have contributed to your being a Ravenclaw?

WEEK 20

RAVENCLAW MOMENTS:
Daily Acts of Wisdom, Wit and Creativity

Monday

Tuesday

Wednesday

Thursday

Friday

Saturday

Sunday

WEEK 20

"*Words are, in my not-so-humble opinion, our most inexhaustible source of magic. Capable of both inflicting injury and remedying it.*"

—Professor Dumbledore, *Harry Potter and the Deathly Hallows - Part 2*

WORDS MATTER!

Write a mantra to help you tap into your inner Ravenclaw.

Use the space below to sketch out your thoughts, and write the final version in the shield on the next page.

MY RAVENCLAW MANTRA

WEEK 21

RAVENCLAW MOMENTS:
Daily Acts of Wisdom, Wit and Creativity

Monday

Tuesday

Wednesday

Thursday

Friday

Saturday

Sunday

WEEK 21

"Welcome to Hogwarts. Now in a few moments, you will pass through the doors and join your classmates, but before you can take your seats, you must be sorted into your houses. They are Gryffindor, Hufflepuff, Ravenclaw and Slytherin. Now while you're here, your house will be like your family."

—Professor McGonagall, *Harry Potter and the Philosopher's Stone*

Think about your closest friends.

What houses do they belong to? Are they the same as you?

How does this affect your relationships?

WEEK 22

RAVENCLAW MOMENTS:
Daily Acts of Wisdom, Wit and Creativity

Monday

Tuesday

Wednesday

Thursday

Friday

Saturday

Sunday

WEEK 22

THINK ABOUT YOUR OWN SOCIAL INTERACTIONS

as a "typical" Ravenclaw. Write about a time you and your friends
acted like Ravenclaws. What did you do? Why is this particular
memory valuable to you?

WEEK 23

RAVENCLAW MOMENTS:
Daily Acts of Wisdom, Wit and Creativity

Monday

Tuesday

Wednesday

Thursday

Friday

Saturday

Sunday

WEEK 23

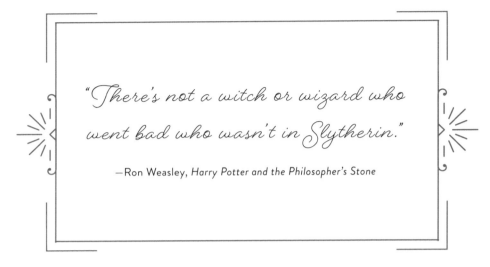

"*There's not a witch or wizard who went bad who wasn't in Slytherin.*"

—Ron Weasley, *Harry Potter and the Philosopher's Stone*

The above quote, spoken by Ron Weasley during the Sorting Ceremony in *Harry Potter and the Philosopher's Stone*, illustrates the fact that stereotypes exist even in the wizarding world. Whether it's the belief that all Slytherins are "bad" or that all Ravenclaws are "eccentric", these stereotypes can be hurtful and unfair. What are some general stereotypes about Ravenclaws that you feel are unfair? What do you say when confronted by them?

WEEK 24

RAVENCLAW MOMENTS:
Daily Acts of Wisdom, Wit and Creativity

Monday

_____

_____

_____

_____

Tuesday

_____

_____

_____

_____

Wednesday

_____

_____

_____

_____

Thursday

Friday

Saturday

Sunday

WEEK 24

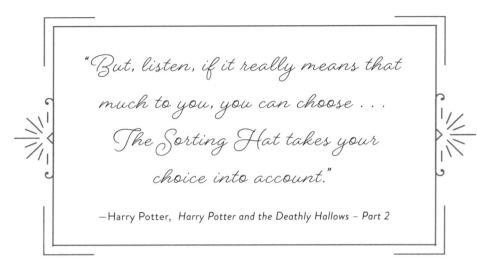

"*But, listen, if it really means that much to you, you can choose . . . The Sorting Hat takes your choice into account.*"

—Harry Potter, *Harry Potter and the Deathly Hallows – Part 2*

In the Harry Potter films, the Sorting Hat was originally planning to put Harry in Slytherin, but he pleaded with the hat not to, and the Sorting Hat accepted his choice. Given the choice, would you choose to be in Ravenclaw? Why or why not?

WEEK 25

RAVENCLAW MOMENTS:

Daily Acts of Wisdom, Wit and Creativity

Monday

Tuesday

Wednesday

Thursday

Friday

Saturday

Sunday

WEEK 25

IN *HARRY POTTER AND THE PHILOSOPHER'S STONE,* Harry, Ron, Hermione and Draco Malfoy are caught out of bed at night and sentenced to detention in the Forbidden Forest. Imagine you've been sentenced to detention at Hogwarts. Based on your personality as a Ravenclaw, what rules do you think you'd be most likely to break and why?

WEEK 26

RAVENCLAW MOMENTS:
Daily Acts of Wisdom, Wit and Creativity

Monday

_____
_____
_____
_____
_____

Tuesday

_____
_____
_____
_____
_____

Wednesday

_____
_____
_____
_____
_____

Thursday

Friday

Saturday

Sunday

WEEK 26

IN *HARRY POTTER AND THE PRISONER OF AZKABAN,*
Professor Lupin teaches the third-year students how to repel a Boggart,
a Dark creature that takes the form of whatever the person fears the most.
Do you have any specific fears that relate to your identity as a Ravenclaw?
Fear of failure? Fear of being second best? Write these down below.
On the following page where it says "Riddikulus!" write what you would use
to repel the Boggart if it turned into what you fear.

ABOVE: The Boggart version of Potions Master Severus Snape, dressed as Neville Longbottom's
grandmother. Design by Jany Temime, drawn by Laurent Guinci.

Riddikulus!

ABOVE: Concept art of the jack-in-the-box version of the Boggart by Rob Bliss.

WEEK 27

RAVENCLAW MOMENTS:
Daily Acts of Wisdom, Wit and Creativity

Monday

Tuesday

Wednesday

Thursday

Friday

Saturday

Sunday

WEEK 27

THINK ABOUT THE HOUSE that you find the most difficult to relate to. What is it about that house that you, as a Ravenclaw, find difficult to understand or appreciate?

WEEK 28

RAVENCLAW MOMENTS:
Daily Acts of Wisdom, Wit and Creativity

Monday

Tuesday

Wednesday

Thursday

Friday

Saturday

Sunday

WEEK 28

WHILE WE NEVER SEE THE RAVENCLAW COMMON ROOM
in the films, we can imagine what it would look like based on the
personality of the house. Look around your own living space. What items
or elements do you feel reflect your tastes as a Ravenclaw?

WEEK 29

RAVENCLAW MOMENTS:

Daily Acts of Wisdom, Wit and Creativity

Monday

Tuesday

Wednesday

Thursday

Friday

Saturday

Sunday

WEEK 29

THE HARRY POTTER FILMS ARE FILLED with examples of romantic pairings between people from different houses, such as Lupin and Tonks, Harry and Cho and Neville and Luna. Consider your ideal romantic partner. Are they in the same house as you? What house do they belong to and why?

WEEK 30

RAVENCLAW MOMENTS:

Daily Acts of Wisdom, Wit and Creativity

Monday

_____
_____
_____
_____
_____

Tuesday

_____
_____
_____
_____
_____

Wednesday

_____
_____
_____
_____
_____

Thursday

Friday

Saturday

Sunday

WEEK 30

IMAGINE YOUR HOUSE JUST WON the House Cup.
How would you celebrate? Use this space to jot down some ideas
for the perfect House Cup party that Ravenclaws everywhere
would love to attend.

WEEK 31

RAVENCLAW MOMENTS:
Daily Acts of Wisdom, Wit and Creativity

Monday

Tuesday

Wednesday

Thursday

Friday

Saturday

Sunday

WHEN FIRST-YEAR HOGWARTS STUDENTS are sorted
into their houses, they are only eleven years old. Do you think you
would have been sorted into Ravenclaw when you were eleven?
How have you changed or grown since then?

WEEK 32

RAVENCLAW MOMENTS:
Daily Acts of Wisdom, Wit and Creativity

Monday

Tuesday

Wednesday

Thursday

Friday

Saturday

Sunday

WEEK 32

IN *HARRY POTTER AND THE HALF-BLOOD PRINCE,*
Harry is given the task of retrieving a memory from Professor Slughorn.
This poses a bit of a problem as the reluctant professor does his best to
avoid Harry once he realises what Harry's trying to do. Harry eventually
solves the problem by taking a dose of Felix Felicis and appealing to
Slughorn's memory of Harry's mother. As a Ravenclaw, how do you solve
problems? When was the last time you used your Ravenclaw qualities to
solve a problem and how?

WEEK 33

RAVENCLAW MOMENTS:

Daily Acts of Wisdom, Wit and Creativity

Monday

Tuesday

Wednesday

Thursday

Friday

Saturday

Sunday

IN *HARRY POTTER AND THE ORDER OF THE PHOENIX,* Harry mistakenly believes a vision sent to him by Lord Voldemort that shows his godfather, Sirius, in danger. Harry rushes to his godfather's aid, an action that eventually leads to Sirius's death. Think about the last time you made a mistake. Were there any aspects of your identity as a Ravenclaw that played a part in the situation? What could you have done differently?

WEEK 34

RAVENCLAW MOMENTS:

Daily Acts of Wisdom, Wit and Creativity

Monday

Tuesday

Wednesday

Thursday

Friday

Saturday

Sunday

WEEK 34

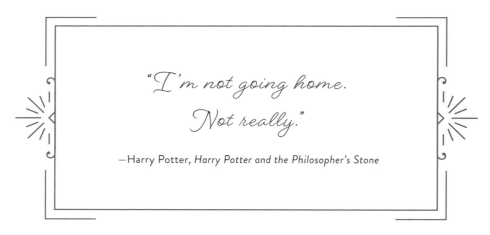

"I'm not going home. Not really."

—Harry Potter, *Harry Potter and the Philosopher's Stone*

Everyone has special places in their lives.
Places where they feel the most like themselves. For Harry,
this is Hogwarts. Think about a space that is important to you
as a Ravenclaw. How does this space bring out those qualities
that symbolise your inner Ravenclaw?

WEEK 35

RAVENCLAW MOMENTS:

Daily Acts of Wisdom, Wit and Creativity

Monday

Tuesday

Wednesday

Thursday

Friday

Saturday

Sunday

WEEK 35

IN *HARRY POTTER AND THE GOBLET OF FIRE*, Harry faces a Hungarian Horntail guarding a golden egg as the first task of the Triwizard Tournament. He uses his broomstick to complete the task, a decision that plays into his assets as a Gryffindor. How would you use your Ravenclaw qualities – wisdom and creativity – to achieve this task?

ABOVE: Concept art of Harry battling the Hungarian Horntail by Paul Catling.

ABOVE: More concept art of Harry and the Hungarian Horntail by Paul Catling.

WEEK 36

RAVENCLAW MOMENTS:
Daily Acts of Wisdom, Wit and Creativity

Monday

Tuesday

Wednesday

Thursday

Friday

Saturday

Sunday

WEEK 36

IN *HARRY POTTER AND THE CHAMBER OF SECRETS,*
Harry discovers he can speak Parseltongue, a skill that frightens him due
to its association with Dark wizards. Have you ever discovered something
about yourself that frightened you? How can you use your assets as a
Ravenclaw to overcome that fear?

WEEK 37

RAVENCLAW MOMENTS:
Daily Acts of Wisdom, Wit and Creativity

Monday

Tuesday

Wednesday

Thursday

Friday

Saturday

Sunday

WEEK 37

WHILE LIFE IN THE HARRY POTTER FILMS never lacks excitement, in the real world, we all get bored from time to time. But boredom can be addressed with just a little creativity. Make a list of ten things you could do right now to challenge, interest or inspire your inner Ravenclaw. Refer back to this the next time you need some inspiration.

1. _____

_____

_____

2. _____

_____

_____

3. _____

_____

_____

4. _____

_____

_____

5. _____

_____

_____

6. _____

_____

_____

7. _____

_____

_____

8. _____

_____

_____

9. _____

_____

_____

10. _____

_____

_____

WEEK 38

RAVENCLAW MOMENTS:
Daily Acts of Wisdom, Wit and Creativity

Monday

Tuesday

Wednesday

Thursday

Friday

Saturday

Sunday

COLOURING MEDITATIONS

Rowena Ravenclaw's diadem is an iconic Ravenclaw artifact. In the film, the diadem is shaped like a raven and features Rowena Ravenclaw's maxim, "Wit beyond measure is man's greatest treasure", inscribed along the bottom edge. What artifacts in your own life represent your identity as a Ravenclaw? Colour in the diadem below, and then decorate the opposite page with illustrations, taped or glued-in ephemera, or other embellishments that symbolise these artifacts.

WEEK 39

RAVENCLAW MOMENTS:
Daily Acts of Wisdom, Wit and Creativity

Monday

_____

_____

_____

_____

Tuesday

_____

_____

_____

_____

Wednesday

_____

_____

_____

_____

Thursday

Friday

Saturday

Sunday

WEEK 39

"For in dreams we enter a world that is entirely our own. Let them swim in the deepest ocean or glide over the highest cloud."

—Professor Dumbledore, *Harry Potter and the Prisoner of Azkaban*

Our dreams can reveal a lot about our inner world. Write down a recent dream you had and how it relates to your identity as a Ravenclaw.

_____

_____

_____

_____

_____

_____

_____

_____

_____

WEEK 40

RAVENCLAW MOMENTS:
Daily Acts of Wisdom, Wit and Creativity

Monday

Tuesday

Wednesday

Thursday

Friday

Saturday

Sunday

WEEK 40

IMAGINE YOU'VE BEEN MADE prefect at Hogwarts.
It's your job to help guide the new first-years in Ravenclaw.
Write down five pieces of advice you would give them to help
them embrace their Ravenclaw identity.

1. _____

_____

_____

_____

_____

_____

2. _____

_____

_____

_____

_____

_____

3. _____
_____
_____
_____
_____
_____

4. _____
_____
_____
_____
_____
_____

5. _____
_____
_____
_____
_____
_____

WEEK 41

RAVENCLAW MOMENTS:
Daily Acts of Wisdom, Wit and Creativity

Monday

_____
_____
_____
_____
_____

Tuesday

_____
_____
_____
_____
_____

Wednesday

_____
_____
_____
_____
_____

Thursday

Friday

Saturday

Sunday

WEEK 41

IN THE HARRY POTTER FILMS, Harry encounters many adult figures who he looks up to and respects – people like Remus Lupin, Minerva McGonagall and even Severus Snape – who help shape his development into a hero. Think about a real-word Ravenclaw in your life who has inspired you. What about this person do you most admire and respect?

WEEK 42

RAVENCLAW MOMENTS:

Daily Acts of Wisdom, Wit and Creativity

Monday

Tuesday

Wednesday

Thursday

Friday

Saturday

Sunday

WEEK 42

"The ones that love us never really leave us. You can always find them. In here."

—Sirius Black, *Harry Potter and the Prisoner of Azkaban*

Think about someone you've lost in your life, either through death or another circumstance. Reflect on your relationship with that person and what they taught you. Did they play any part in your development as a Ravenclaw? How so?

WEEK 43

RAVENCLAW MOMENTS:
Daily Acts of Wisdom, Wit and Creativity

Monday

_____

_____

_____

_____

Tuesday

_____

_____

_____

_____

Wednesday

_____

_____

_____

_____

Thursday

Friday

Saturday

Sunday

WEEK 43

THE WIZARDING WORLD IS FULL of an astonishing array of magical creatures: dragons, Hippogriffs, house-elves, centaurs, phoenixes and more. What creature do you think embodies similar traits to those of Ravenclaw house? How can you bring the spirit of that creature into your daily life?

ABOVE LEFT: Concept art of a Thestral by Rob Bliss.
ABOVE RIGHT: Concept art of Fawkes the phoenix by Adam Brockbank.

CLOCKWISE FROM TOP LEFT: Concept art of Aragog in his lair by Adam Brockbank;
a centaur draws his bow, also by Adam Brockbank; Harry riding Buckbeak the
Hippogriff, art by Dermot Power.

WEEK 44

RAVENCLAW MOMENTS:
Daily Acts of Wisdom, Wit and Creativity

Monday

Tuesday

Wednesday

Thursday

Friday

Saturday

Sunday

WEEK 44

IN THE HARRY POTTER FILMS, there are moments of great danger and grief, especially in the later films as the wizarding world becomes enveloped in a devastating war against Lord Voldemort. In the real world, everyone deals with stress, pain and emotional upheaval from time to time. That's why it's important to prioritise self-care. As a Ravenclaw, what does self-care mean to you? How do you take care of yourself when faced with stress or pain?

WEEK 45

RAVENCLAW MOMENTS:
Daily Acts of Wisdom, Wit and Creativity

Monday

_____

_____

_____

_____

Tuesday

_____

_____

_____

_____

Wednesday

_____

_____

_____

_____

Thursday

Friday

Saturday

Sunday

WEEK 45

YOU'VE JUST LANDED A MAJOR JOB INTERVIEW.

How can you use your assets as a Ravenclaw to get the job?

Make a list of five things you can do to prepare.

1. _____

2. _____

3. _____

4. _____

5. _____

WEEK 46

RAVENCLAW MOMENTS:
Daily Acts of Wisdom, Wit and Creativity

Monday

_____
_____
_____
_____

Tuesday

_____
_____
_____
_____

Wednesday

_____
_____
_____
_____

Thursday

Friday

Saturday

Sunday

WEEK 46

THERE ARE SEVERAL GREAT EXAMPLES of Ravenclaw heroes in the Harry Potter films: Luna Lovegood, Cho Chang, not to mention all the Ravenclaws that joined Dumbledore's Army. What do you think defines a Ravenclaw hero? How can you, as a Ravenclaw, be a hero to someone in your life?

WEEK 47

RAVENCLAW MOMENTS:

Daily Acts of Wisdom, Wit and Creativity

Monday

Tuesday

Wednesday

Thursday

Friday

Saturday

Sunday

WEEK 47

IN *HARRY POTTER AND THE CHAMBER OF SECRETS*,
Draco Malfoy goads Ron Weasley into attacking him by calling Hermione a
foul name, an act that plays into Ron's Gryffindor qualities of chivalry and
determination. Has anybody ever used your traits as a Ravenclaw against you?
What could you have done differently?

WEEK 48

RAVENCLAW MOMENTS:
Daily Acts of Wisdom, Wit and Creativity

Monday

_____

_____

_____

_____

_____

Tuesday

_____

_____

_____

_____

_____

Wednesday

_____

_____

_____

_____

_____

Thursday

Friday

Saturday

Sunday

WEEK 48

IN *HARRY POTTER AND THE ORDER OF THE PHOENIX*, Harry and his friends start Dumbledore's Army, a secret student group dedicated to fighting Dolores Umbridge's rules and learning practical Defence Against the Dark Arts skills. As a Ravenclaw, how can you stand up for what you believe in? What kind of steps do you feel you can take to contribute?

WEEK 49

RAVENCLAW MOMENTS:
Daily Acts of Wisdom, Wit and Creativity

Monday

Tuesday

Wednesday

Thursday

_____
_____
_____
_____
_____

Friday

_____
_____
_____
_____
_____

Saturday

_____
_____
_____
_____
_____

Sunday

_____
_____
_____
_____
_____

WEEK 49

"We are only as strong as we are united, as weak as we are divided."

—Professor Dumbledore, *Harry Potter and the Goblet of Fire*

Think of a time you were in conflict with someone who embodies the characteristics of another house. How were you able to resolve the situation? Did your qualities as a Ravenclaw prove to be an asset or an obstacle?

WEEK 50

RAVENCLAW MOMENTS:

Daily Acts of Wisdom, Wit and Creativity

Monday

Tuesday

Wednesday

Thursday

_____
_____
_____
_____
_____

Friday

_____
_____
_____
_____
_____

Saturday

_____
_____
_____
_____
_____

Sunday

_____
_____
_____
_____
_____

WEEK 50

AS EVERYONE KNOWS, the traits of Ravenclaw are wisdom, wit and creativity. After fifty weeks of reflection and development, which of these traits do you identify with the most? Which do you identify with the least? Are there any additional traits that you feel match the Ravenclaw profile that are not talked about as much?

WEEK 51

RAVENCLAW MOMENTS:

Daily Acts of Wisdom, Wit and Creativity

Monday

_____
_____
_____
_____
_____

Tuesday

_____
_____
_____
_____
_____

Wednesday

_____
_____
_____
_____
_____

Thursday

Friday

Saturday

Sunday

WEEK 51

"We've got one thing Voldemort doesn't have. Something worth fighting for."

—Harry Potter, *Harry Potter and the Order of the Phoenix*

Everybody believes in fighting for something.

As a Ravenclaw, what do you think is worth fighting for?

How do you fight for it?

WEEK 52

RAVENCLAW MOMENTS:
Daily Acts of Wisdom, Wit and Creativity

Monday

Tuesday

Wednesday

Thursday

Friday

Saturday

Sunday

WEEK 52

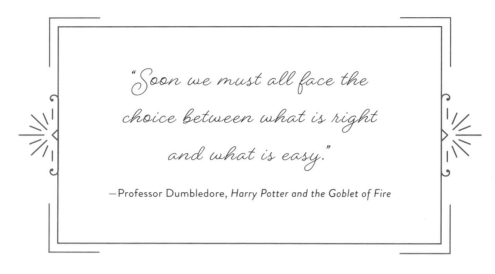

"*Soon we must all face the choice between what is right and what is easy.*"

—Professor Dumbledore, *Harry Potter and the Goblet of Fire*

For this final prompt, reflect on what you've learned.

How do your qualities as a Ravenclaw help you make the right choices?

INSIGHT
EDITIONS

PO Box 3088
San Rafael, CA 94912
www.insighteditions.com

 Find us on Facebook: www.facebook.com/InsightEditions
 Follow us on Twitter: @insighteditions

Copyright © 2020 Warner Bros. Entertainment Inc. WIZARDING WORLD characters, names and related indicia are © & TM Warner Bros. Entertainment Inc. WB SHIELD: © & TM WBEI. Publishing Rights © JKR. (s20)

All rights reserved. Published under license by Studio Press, an imprint of Bonnier Books UK.

The publisher does not have any control over and does not assume any responsibility for author or third-party websites or their content.

No part of this publication may be reproduced, stored in a retrieval system, or transmitted in any form or by any means, electronic, mechanical, photocopying, recording or otherwise without written permission of the publisher. For information regarding permissions, write to Studio Press, The Plaza, 535 King's Road, London SW10 0SZ.

This book is a work of fiction. Names, characters, places and incidents are either the product of the author's imagination or are used fictitiously, and any resemblance to actual persons, living or dead, business establishments, events, or locales is entirely coincidental.

 Library of Congress Cataloging-in-Publication Data available.

ISBN: 978-1-78741-957-5

Publisher: Raoul Goff
Creative Director: Chrissy Kwasnik
Senior Designer: Ashley Quackenbush
Editorial Assistant: Anna Wostenberg
Production Editor: Jennifer Bentham
Text by Hilary VandenBroek

Associate Publisher: Vanessa Lopez
VP of Manufacturing: Alix Nicholaeff
Editor: Hilary VandenBroek
Managing Editor: Lauren LaPera
Production Manager: Andy Harper

ROOTS of PEACE   REPLANTED PAPER

Insight Editions, in association with Roots of Peace, will plant two trees for each tree used in the manufacturing of this book. Roots of Peace is an internationally renowned humanitarian organization dedicated to eradicating land mines worldwide and converting war-torn lands into productive farms and wildlife habitats. Roots of Peace will plant two million fruit and nut trees in Afghanistan and provide farmers there with the skills and support necessary for sustainable land use.

Manufactured in China by Insight Editions